ILLUSTRATED BY

KATE BROWN

Published by
SelfMadeHero
A division of Metro Media Ltd
5 Upper Wimpole Street
London W1G 6BP
www.selfmadehero.com

This edition published 2008

Illustrator: Kate Brown
Text Adaptor: Richard Appignanesi
Designer: Andy Huckle
Textual Consultant: Nick de Somogyi
Publisher: Emma Hayley

ISBN-13: 978-0-9552856-4-6

10 9 8 7 6 5 4 3 2 1
Printed and bound in China

Theseus, Duke of Athens

"Now, fair Hippolyta,
our nuptial hour
draws on apace."

"Four nights will quickly
dream away the time."

Hippolyta, Queen of the Amazons

"She is mine, and all my right of her I do estate unto Demetrius."

Philostrate, Master of the Revels

"Make choice of which your highness will see first."

Hermia, daughter of Egeus

"Lysander and myself will fly this place."

Helena, in love with Demetrius
“The more I love, the more he hateth me.”
Demetrius, Hermia's suitor
“Relent, sweet Hermia. Lysander, yield to my certain right.”
Lysander, in love with Hermia
“I am beloved of beauteous Hermia.”

Titania, Queen of the Fairies

"The fairy land buys not the child of me."

"Ill met by moonlight, proud Titania."

Oberon, King of the Fairies

"I am that
merry wanderer
of the night..."
Cobweb
Moth
Mustardseed
Peaseblossom
Puck, or Robin Goodfellow, Oberon's goblin servant

"Nay, faith, let not me play a woman!"

Francis Flute, a bellows-mender

"What beard were I best to play it in?"

Nick Bottom, a weaver

Peter Quince, a carpenter

"Nick Bottom, you are set down for Pyramus."

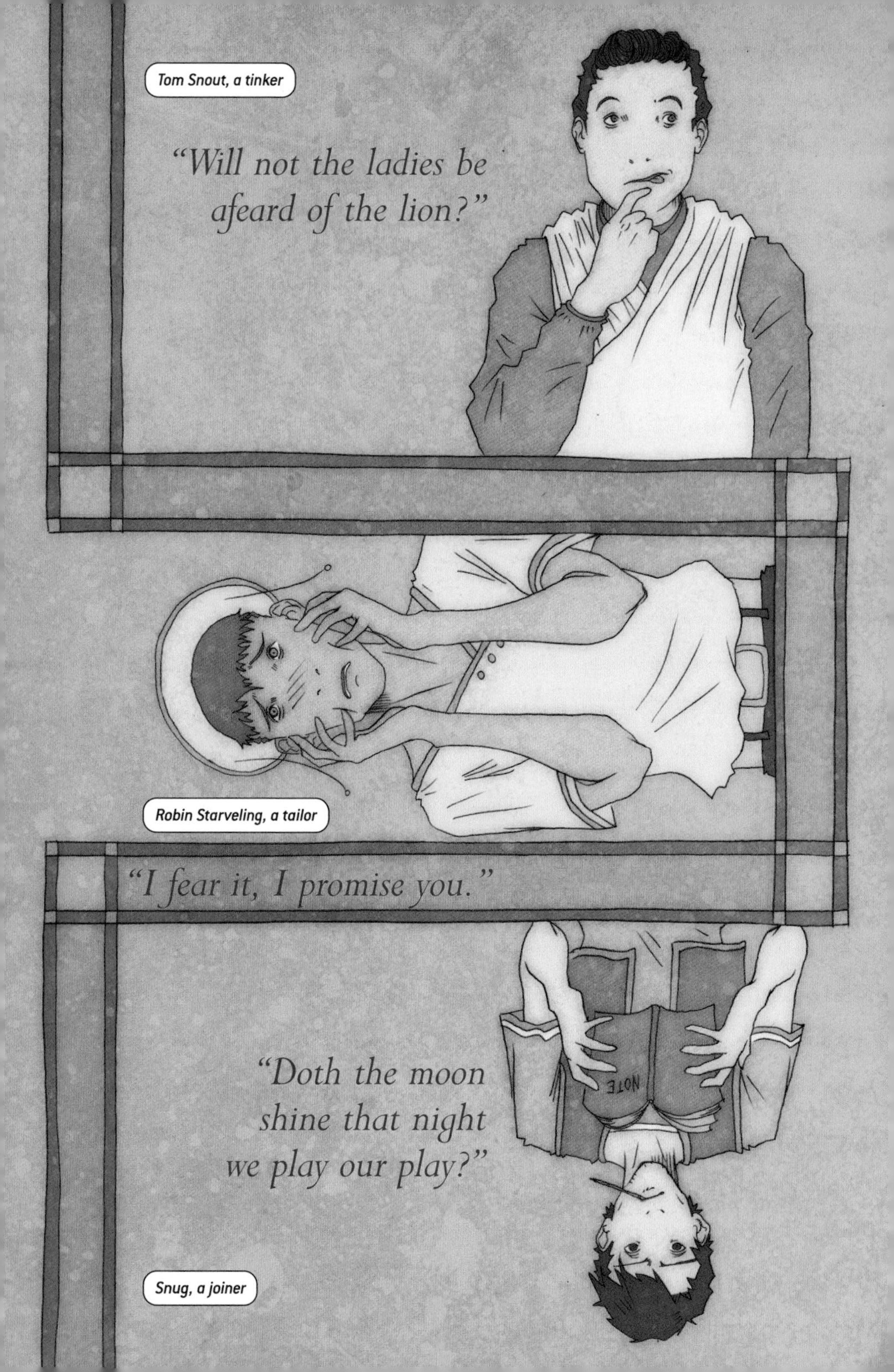
Tom Snout, a tinker
"Will not the ladies be afeard of the lion?"
Robin Starveling, a tailor
"I fear it, I promise you."
"Doth the moon shine that night we play our play?"
Snug, a joiner

Athens – where modern technology meets ancient tradition...

On a Midsummer's Night...

"We the globe can compass soon, swifter than the wandering moon..."

NOW, FAIR HIPPOLYTA, OUR NUPTIAL HOUR DRAWS ON APACE.
FOUR HAPPY DAYS BRING IN ANOTHER MOON.
BUT O, HOW SLOW THIS OLD MOON WANES! SHE LINGERS MY DESIRES...
FOUR NIGHTS WILL QUICKLY DREAM AWAY THE TIME.
AND THEN THE MOON SHALL BEHOLD THE NIGHT OF OUR SOLEMNITIES.

GO, PHILOSTRATE, STIR UP THE ATHENIAN YOUTH TO MERRIMENTS.
AWAKE THE NIMBLE SPIRIT OF MIRTH.

HIPPOLYTA, I WOOED THEE WITH MY SWORD AND WON THY LOVE DOING THEE INJURIES.
BUT I WILL WED THEE WITH POMP, TRIUMPH AND REVELLING.
INCOMING CALL!

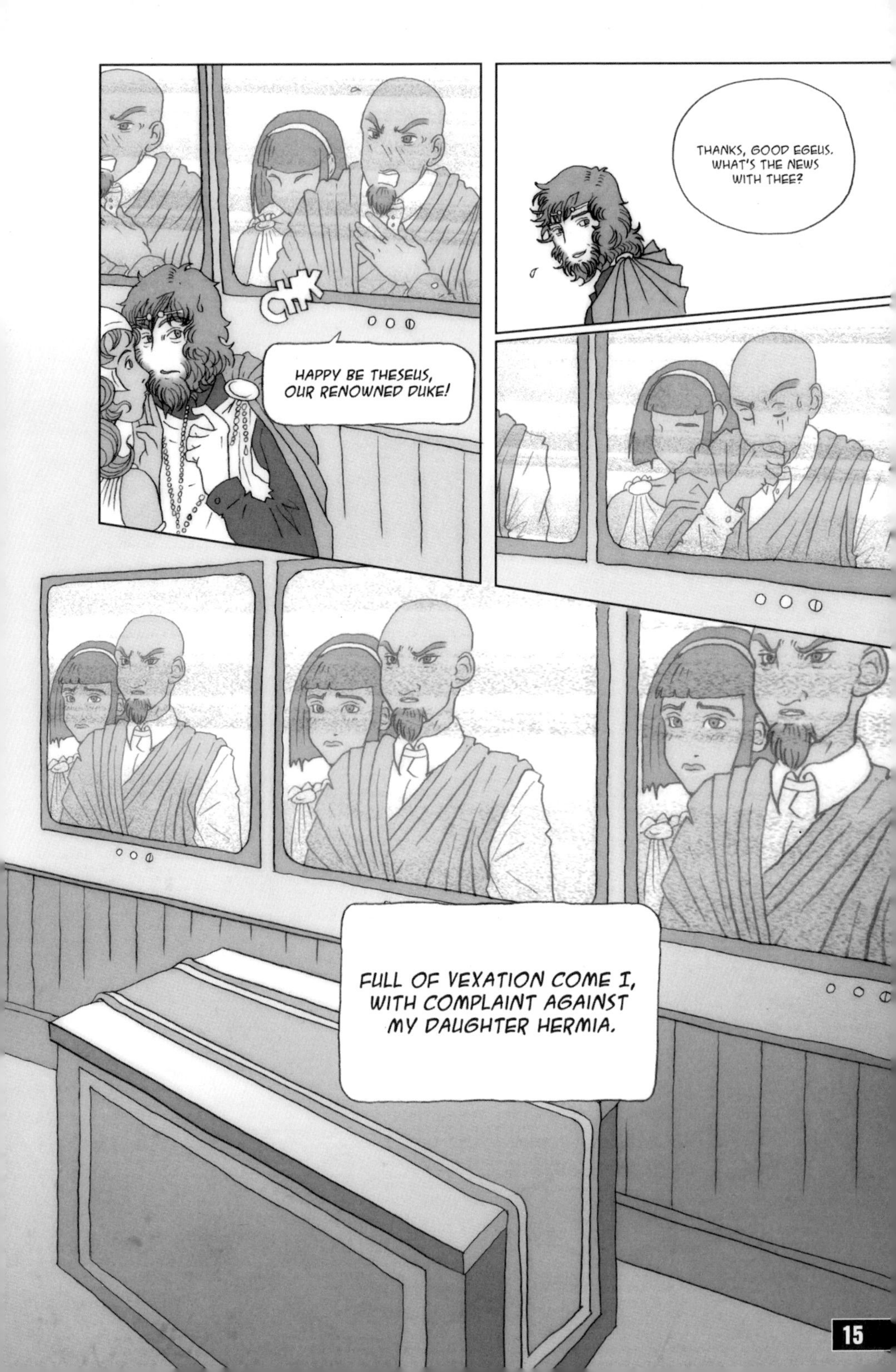
CHK
HAPPY BE THESEUS, OUR RENOWNED DUKE!
THANKS, GOOD EGEUS. WHAT'S THE NEWS WITH THEE?
FULL OF VEXATION COME I, WITH COMPLAINT AGAINST MY DAUGHTER HERMIA.

STAND FORTH, DEMETRIUS!
MY NOBLE LORD, THIS MAN HATH MY CONSENT TO MARRY HER.
STAND FORTH, LYSANDER!
THIS MAN HATH BEWITCHED THE BOSOM OF MY CHILD.

LYSANDER...
THOU HAST INTERCHANGED LOVE-TOKENS WITH MY CHILD.
THOU HAST BY MOONLIGHT AT HER WINDOW
SUNG VERSES OF FEIGNING LOVE.

WITH CUNNING HAST THOU FILCHED MY DAUGHTER'S HEART,
TURNED HER OBEDIENCE,
WHICH IS DUE TO ME,
TO STUBBORN HARSHNESS.

MY GRACIOUS DUKE,
BE IT SO SHE WILL NOT HERE CONSENT TO MARRY WITH DEMETRIUS,
I BEG THE ANCIENT PRIVILEGE OF ATHENS.
AS SHE IS MINE, I MAY DISPOSE OF HER –
WHICH SHALL BE EITHER TO THIS GENTLEMAN OR TO HER DEATH,
ACCORDING TO OUR LAW.

WHAT SAY YOU, HERMIA?
TO YOU, YOUR FATHER SHOULD BE AS A GOD.
YOU ARE BUT AS A FORM IN WAX BY HIM IMPRINTED.
DEMETRIUS IS A WORTHY GENTLEMAN.
SO IS LYSANDER.

I WOULD MY FATHER LOOKED BUT WITH MY EYES.
RATHER YOUR EYES MUST WITH HIS JUDGEMENT LOOK.
PARDON ME.
I KNOW NOT BY WHAT POWER I AM MADE BOLD.
I BESEECH YOUR GRACE THAT I MAY KNOW THE WORST THAT MAY BEFALL ME IN THIS CASE,
IF I REFUSE TO WED DEMETRIUS.
EITHER TO DIE THE DEATH OR TO ABJURE FOR EVER THE SOCIETY OF MEN.

THEREFORE, FAIR HERMIA, QUESTION YOUR DESIRES.
KNOW WHETHER, IF YOU YIELD NOT TO YOUR FATHER'S CHOICE,
YOU CAN ENDURE TO LIVE A BARREN SISTER ALL YOUR LIFE,
CHANTING FAINT HYMNS TO THE COLD FRUITLESS MOON.

SO WILL I LIVE,
SO DIE, MY LORD,
ERE I WILL YIELD MY VIRGIN PATENT UP UNTO HIS LORDSHIP,

WHOSE UNWISHED YOKE MY SOUL CONSENTS **NOT** TO GIVE SOVEREIGNTY.

TAKE TIME TO PAUSE, AND BY THE NEXT NEW MOON,
EITHER PREPARE TO DIE FOR DISOBEDIENCE TO YOUR FATHER'S WILL,

OR ELSE TO WED DEMETRIUS...

OR TO PROTEST AUSTERITY AND SINGLE LIFE.

RELENT, SWEET HERMIA.
LYSANDER, YIELD THY CRAZED TITLE TO MY CERTAIN RIGHT.
YOU HAVE HER FATHER'S LOVE, DEMETRIUS: DO YOU MARRY HIM!
SCORNFUL LYSANDER!
TRUE, HE HATH MY LOVE, AND WHAT IS MINE MY LOVE SHALL RENDER HIM.
AND SHE IS MINE, AND ALL MY RIGHT OF HER I DO ESTATE UNTO DEMETRIUS.

MY LORD, MY LOVE IS MORE THAN HIS,
MY FORTUNES EVERY WAY AS FAIRLY RANKED.
AND, WHICH IS MORE THAN ALL THESE BOASTS CAN BE – I AM BELOVED OF BEAUTEOUS HERMIA.
WHY SHOULD NOT I THEN PROSECUTE MY RIGHT?

DEMETRIUS MADE LOVE TO NEDAR'S DAUGHTER, HELENA,
AND WON HER SOUL.
AND SHE, SWEET LADY,
DEVOUTLY DOTES UPON THIS INCONSTANT MAN.

I MUST CONFESS THAT I HAVE HEARD SO MUCH,
AND WITH DEMETRIUS THOUGHT TO HAVE SPOKE THEREOF...
BUT, BEING OVER-FULL OF SELF-AFFAIRS, MY MIND DID LOSE IT.
FOR YOU, FAIR HERMIA, LOOK YOU TO FIT YOUR FANCIES TO YOUR FATHER'S WILL,
OR ELSE THE LAW OF ATHENS YIELDS YOU UP TO DEATH OR TO A VOW OF SINGLE LIFE.

COME, MY HIPPOLYTA.
DEMETRIUS AND EGEUS, GO ALONG. I MUST CONFER WITH YOU OF SOMETHING THAT CONCERNS YOURSELVES.
WITH DUTY AND DESIRE WE FOLLOW YOU.

AY ME!
THE COURSE OF TRUE LOVE NEVER DID RUN SMOOTH.
THEN LET US TEACH OUR TRIAL PATIENCE, BECAUSE IT IS A CUSTOMARY CROSS,
AS DUE TO LOVE AS THOUGHTS AND DREAMS AND SIGHS, WISHES AND TEARS.

THEREFORE HEAR ME, HERMIA.
I HAVE A WIDOW AUNT, A DOWAGER OF GREAT REVENUE, AND SHE HATH NO CHILD.
FROM ATHENS IS HER HOUSE REMOTE SEVEN LEAGUES.
THERE MAY I MARRY THEE, AND TO THAT PLACE THE SHARP ATHENIAN LAW CANNOT PURSUE US.

IF THOU LOV'ST ME, STEAL FORTH THY FATHER'S HOUSE TOMORROW NIGHT.
AND IN THE WOOD, WHERE I DID MEET THEE ONCE WITH HELENA, THERE WILL I STAY FOR THEE.

MY GOOD LYSANDER!
I SWEAR TO THEE BY ALL THE VOWS THAT EVER MEN HAVE BROKE –
IN NUMBER MORE THAN EVER WOMEN SPOKE –
IN THAT SAME PLACE TOMORROW TRULY WILL I MEET WITH THEE.

KEEP PROMISE, LOVE.
LOOK, HERE COMES HELENA.
GOD SPEED, FAIR HELENA!
CALL YOU ME FAIR? THAT "FAIR" AGAIN UNSAY.
DEMETRIUS LOVES YOUR FAIR. O HAPPY FAIR!
O, TEACH ME HOW YOU LOOK, AND WITH WHAT ART
YOU SWAY THE MOTION OF DEMETRIUS' HEART.

THE MORE I HATE, THE MORE HE FOLLOWS ME.
THE MORE I LOVE, THE MORE HE HATETH ME.
HIS FOLLY, HELENA, IS NO FAULT OF MINE.
NONE BUT YOUR BEAUTY. WOULD THAT FAULT WERE MINE!

TAKE COMFORT.
HE NO MORE SHALL SEE MY FACE.
LYSANDER AND MYSELF WILL FLY THIS PLACE.
HELEN, TO YOU OUR MINDS WE WILL UNFOLD.
TOMORROW NIGHT THROUGH ATHENS' GATES HAVE WE DEVISED TO STEAL.

AND IN THE WOOD, THERE MY LYSANDER
AND MYSELF SHALL MEET.

AND THENCE FROM ATHENS TURN AWAY
OUR EYES TO SEEK NEW FRIENDS
AND STRANGER COMPANIES.

KEEP WORD, LYSANDER.

I WILL, MY HERMIA.
HELENA, ADIEU.

THROUGH ATHENS I AM
THOUGHT AS FAIR AS SHE,
BUT WHAT OF THAT?
DEMETRIUS THINKS NOT SO.
LOVE LOOKS NOT WITH THE
EYES BUT WITH THE MIND,
AND THEREFORE IS WINGED
CUPID PAINTED BLIND.
FOR ERE DEMETRIUS
LOOKED ON HERMIA'S
EYNE,
HE HAILED DOWN
OATHS THAT HE
WAS ONLY MINE...

I WILL GO TELL
HIM OF FAIR
HERMIA'S FLIGHT.
THEN TO THE WOOD WILL
HE TOMORROW NIGHT
PURSUE HER.
AND FOR THIS INTELLIGENCE
IF I HAVE THANKS,
IT IS A DEAR EXPENSE.
BUT HEREIN MEAN
I TO HAVE HIS SIGHT
BACK AGAIN.

HERE IS THE SCROLL OF EVERY MAN'S NAME WHICH IS THOUGHT FIT TO PLAY IN OUR INTERLUDE BEFORE THE DUKE AND THE DUCHESS ON HIS WEDDING-DAY.
FIRST, GOOD PETER QUINCE, SAY WHAT THE PLAY TREATS ON, THEN READ THE NAMES OF THE ACTORS.
OUR PLAY IS...
THWAK
THE MOST LAMENTABLE COMEDY, AND MOST CRUEL DEATH OF PYRAMUS AND THISBE.

A VERY GOOD PIECE OF WORK,
I ASSURE YOU.
NOW, CALL FORTH YOUR ACTORS BY THE SCROLL.
BASH
BASH
FSSSS
REJECTED!
NICK BOTTOM, THE WEAVER, YOU ARE SET DOWN FOR PYRAMUS.
WHAT IS PYRAMUS? A LOVER OR A TYRANT?
A LOVER THAT KILLS HIMSELF MOST GALLANTLY FOR LOVE.

THAT WILL ASK SOME TEARS IN THE TRUE PERFORMING OF IT.
LET THE AUDIENCE LOOK TO THEIR EYES –
I WILL MOVE STORMS!
FRANCIS FLUTE, THE BELLOWS-MENDER, YOU MUST TAKE THISBE.
WHAT IS THISBE? A WANDERING KNIGHT?

IT IS THE LADY THAT PYRAMUS MUST LOVE.
REJECTED!
NAY, FAITH, LET NOT ME PLAY A WOMAN!
I HAVE A BEARD COMING.
YOU SHALL PLAY IT IN A MASK AND SPEAK AS SMALL AS YOU WILL.
LET ME PLAY THISBE TOO.
I'LL SPEAK IN A MONSTROUS LITTLE VOICE.
NO, NO,
YOU MUST PLAY PYRAMUS,
AND FLUTE, YOU THISBE.

ROBIN STARVELING, THE TAILOR, YOU MUST PLAY THISBE'S MOTHER.
TOM SNOUT, THE TINKER, PYRAMUS'S FATHER.
MYSELF, THISBE'S FATHER.
SNUG, THE JOINER, YOU THE LION'S PART.
NOTE
AND, I HOPE, HERE IS A PLAY FITTED.
NOTE
NOTE

HAVE YOU THE LION'S PART WRITTEN?
IF IT BE, GIVE IT ME, FOR I AM SLOW OF STUDY.
BUZZ BUZZ
YOU MAY DO IT EXTEMPORE, FOR IT IS NOTHING BUT ROARING.
NOTE
"EX TEM PO RE."
LET ME PLAY THE LION TOO. I WILL ROAR THAT I WILL MAKE THE DUKE SAY,
"LET HIM ROAR AGAIN, LET HIM ROAR AGAIN."
BUZZZZ
YOU WOULD FRIGHT THE DUCHESS AND THE LADIES THAT THEY WOULD SHRIEK...
AND THAT WERE ENOUGH TO HANG US ALL!

THAT WOULD HANG US, EVERY MOTHER'S SON!
BUT I WILL ROAR YOU AS GENTLY AS ANY SUCKING DOVE. I WILL ROAR YOU AS 'TWERE ANY NIGHTINGALE.
YOU CAN PLAY NO PART BUT PYRAMUS.
WHAT BEARD WERE I BEST TO PLAY IT IN?
WHY, WHAT YOU WILL.

HERE ARE YOUR PARTS.
MEET ME IN THE PALACE WOOD, A MILE WITHOUT THE TOWN, BY MOONLIGHT.
THERE WILL WE REHEARSE.
FOR IF WE MEET IN THE CITY, WE SHALL BE DOGGED WITH COMPANY, AND OUR DEVICES KNOWN.
I PRAY YOU, FAIL ME NOT.
WE WILL MEET AND THERE REHEARSE MOST OBSCENELY AND COURAGEOUSLY.
TAKE PAINS,
BE PERFECT,
ADIEU.

HOW NOW, SPIRIT!
WHITHER WANDER YOU?

I DO WANDER EVERYWHERE, SWIFTER THAN THE MOON'S SPHERE.

I SERVE THE FAIRY QUEEN.

FAREWELL, I'LL BE GONE. OUR QUEEN AND ALL OUR ELVES COME HERE ANON.

THE KING DOTH KEEP HIS REVELS HERE TONIGHT.
TAKE HEED THE QUEEN COME NOT WITHIN HIS SIGHT...
BECAUSE SHE HATH A LOVELY BOY AND JEALOUS OBERON WOULD HAVE THE CHILD KNIGHT OF HIS TRAIN.
BUT SHE WITHHOLDS THE LOVED BOY AND MAKES HIM ALL HER JOY.

YOU ARE THAT SHREWD AND KNAVISH SPRITE CALLED ROBIN GOODFELLOW.
ARE NOT YOU HE THAT MISLEAD NIGHT-WANDERERS, LAUGHING AT THEIR HARM?
THOSE THAT HOBGOBLIN CALL YOU AND SWEET PUCK,
YOU DO THEIR WORK AND THEY SHALL HAVE GOOD LUCK.

I AM THAT MERRY WANDERER OF THE NIGHT.
I JEST TO OBERON AND MAKE HIM SMILE.
THE WHOLE CHOIR HOLD THEIR HIPS AND LAUGH IN THEIR MIRTH AND SWEAR A MERRIER HOUR WAS NEVER WASTED THERE.
BUT, ROOM, FAIRY!
HERE COMES OBERON.
AND HERE MY MISTRESS.
WOULD THAT HE WERE GONE!

ILL MET BY MOONLIGHT, PROUD TITANIA.
WHAT, JEALOUS OBERON?
AM NOT I THY LORD?

WHY ART THOU HERE
COME FROM INDIA?
BUT THAT THE AMAZON, YOUR BUSKINED MISTRESS AND YOUR WARRIOR LOVE, TO THESEUS MUST BE WEDDED.
YOU COME TO GIVE THEIR BED JOY AND PROSPERITY.
HOW CANST THOU FOR SHAME,
TITANIA,
GLANCE AT MY CREDIT WITH HIPPOLYTA,
KNOWING I KNOW THY LOVE TO THESEUS?

THESE ARE THE FORGERIES OF JEALOUSY – WITH THY BRAWLS THOU HAST DISTURBED OUR SPORT.
THEREFORE THE WINDS IN REVENGE HAVE SUCKED UP FROM THE SEA CONTAGIOUS FOGS.

EVERY
PELTING RIVER –
OVERBORNE THEIR
CONTINENTS.
THE GREEN CORN HATH ROTTED,
THE FOLD STANDS EMPTY,
AND CROWS ARE FATTED.
THE HUMAN
MORTALS WANT
THEIR WINTER CHEER.

RHEUMATIC DISEASES DO ABOUND.
WE SEE THE SEASONS ALTER.
HOARY-HEADED FROSTS FALL IN THE FRESH LAP OF THE CRIMSON ROSE.
THE SPRING,
THE SUMMER,
THE CHILDING AUTUMN,
ANGRY WINTER, CHANGE
AND THE MAZED WORLD NOW KNOWS NOT WHICH IS WHICH.

THIS PROGENY OF EVILS COMES FROM OUR DEBATE.
THE FAIRY LAND BUYS NOT THE CHILD OF ME.
DO YOU AMEND IT THEN!
IT LIES IN YOU.
I DO BUT BEG A LITTLE CHANGELING BOY TO BE MY HENCHMAN.

HIS MOTHER WAS A VOTARESS OF MY ORDER.
IN THE SPICED INDIAN AIR, BY NIGHT,
OFTEN SHE GOSSIPED BY MY SIDE AND SAT WITH ME ON NEPTUNE'S YELLOW SANDS.

BUT SHE, BEING MORTAL, OF THAT BOY DID DIE.

FOR HER SAKE DO I REAR UP HER BOY,

AND FOR HER SAKE I WILL ***NOT*** PART WITH HIM.

HOW LONG WITHIN THIS WOOD INTEND YOU STAY?
PERCHANCE TILL AFTER THESEUS' WEDDING-DAY.
IF YOU WILL SEE OUR MOONLIGHT REVELS, GO WITH US. IF NOT, SHUN ME, AND I WILL SPARE YOUR HAUNTS.

GIVE ME THAT BOY AND I WILL GO WITH THEE.
NOT FOR THY FAIRY KINGDOM.
FAIRIES, AWAY!
WE SHALL CHIDE DOWNRIGHT IF I LONGER STAY.
WELL, GO THY WAY!
THOU SHALT NOT FROM THIS GROVE TILL I TORMENT THEE FOR THIS INJURY.

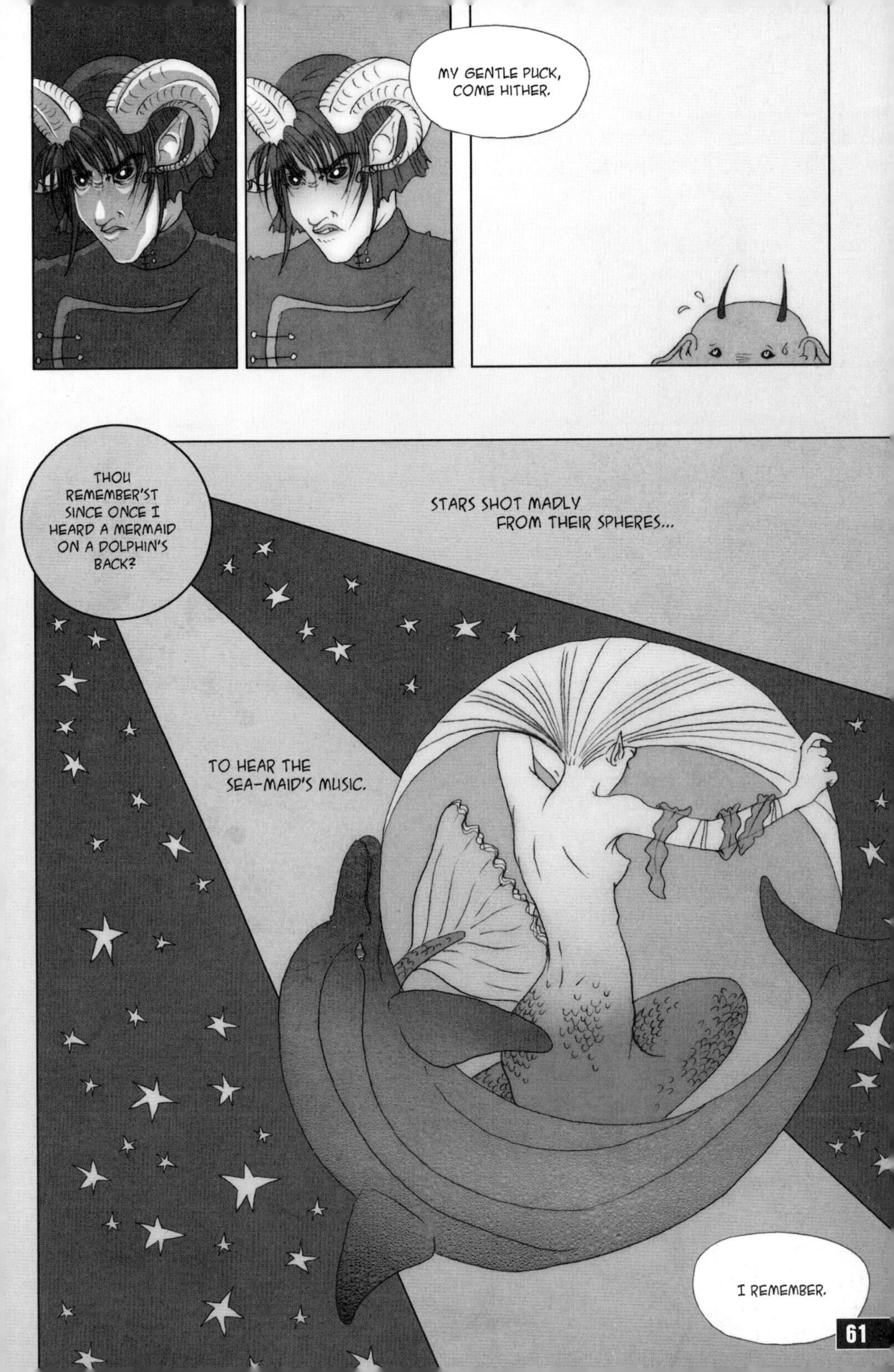
MY GENTLE PUCK, COME HITHER.
THOU REMEMBER'ST SINCE ONCE I HEARD A MERMAID ON A DOLPHIN'S BACK?
STARS SHOT MADLY FROM THEIR SPHERES...
TO HEAR THE SEA-MAID'S MUSIC.
I REMEMBER.

THAT VERY TIME I SAW,
FLYING BETWEEN THE
COLD MOON AND THE EARTH,

CUPID ALL ARMED.

A CERTAIN AIM HE
TOOK AT A FAIR VESTAL

AND LOOSED HIS LOVE-SHAFT
SMARTLY FROM HIS BOW.

BUT CUPID'S FIERY SHAFT
QUENCHED IN THE CHASTE BEAMS
OF THE WATERY MOON...

AND THE IMPERIAL VOTARESS
PASSED ON, FANCY-FREE.

YET MARKED I WHERE THE BOLT OF CUPID FELL UPON A LITTLE FLOWER, BEFORE MILK-WHITE, NOW PURPLE WITH LOVE'S WOUND.

FETCH ME THAT FLOWER.

THE JUICE OF IT ON SLEEPING EYELIDS WILL MAKE OR MAN OR WOMAN MADLY DOTE UPON THE NEXT LIVE CREATURE THAT IT SEES.

I'LL WATCH TITANIA
WHEN SHE IS ASLEEP
AND DROP THE LIQUOR
OF IT IN HER EYES.
THE NEXT THING
SHE WAKING
LOOKS UPON...
BE IT LION, BEAR,
OR WOLF, OR BULL,
OR BUSY APE...
SHE SHALL PURSUE
IT WITH THE
SOUL OF LOVE.

ERE I TAKE THIS CHARM FROM OFF HER SIGHT,
I'LL MAKE HER RENDER UP HER PAGE TO ME.
BUT WHO COMES HERE?
I AM INVISIBLE, AND I WILL OVERHEAR THEIR CONFERENCE.

I LOVE THEE NOT, THEREFORE PURSUE ME NOT.
WHERE IS LYSANDER AND FAIR HERMIA?
THE ONE I'LL SLAY, THE OTHER SLAYETH ME.
HENCE! GET THEE GONE, AND FOLLOW ME NO MORE.
YOU DRAW ME, YOU HARD-HEARTED ADAMANT!
FOR MY HEART IS TRUE AS STEEL.
DO I NOT IN PLAINEST TRUTH TELL YOU, I DO NOT, NOR CANNOT LOVE YOU?

AND EVEN FOR THAT DO I LOVE YOU THE MORE. I AM YOUR SPANIEL, DEMETRIUS –
SPURN ME,
STRIKE ME,
NEGLECT ME,
ONLY GIVE ME LEAVE TO FOLLOW YOU.
I AM SICK WHEN I DO LOOK ON YOU.
AND I AM SICK WHEN I LOOK NOT ON YOU.

YOU DO IMPEACH YOUR MODESTY TOO MUCH
TO LEAVE THE CITY AND COMMIT YOURSELF INTO THE HANDS
OF ONE THAT
LOVES YOU NOT.
YOUR VIRTUE IS MY PRIVILEGE,
FOR YOU IN MY RESPECT ARE ALL THE WORLD.
THEN HOW CAN IT BE SAID I AM ALONE,
WHEN ALL THE WORLD IS HERE TO LOOK ON ME?

I'LL RUN FROM THEE AND LEAVE THEE TO THE MERCY OF WILD BEASTS.
THE WILDEST HATH NOT SUCH A HEART AS YOU.
RUN WHEN YOU WILL,
FWOMP
THE DOVE PURSUES THE GRIFFIN,
THE MILD HIND MAKES SPEED TO CATCH THE TIGER.

LET ME GO!
OR IF THOU FOLLOW ME, BELIEVE I SHALL DO THEE MISCHIEF IN THE WOOD.
DEMETRIUS!
AY, IN THE TEMPLE, IN THE TOWN, THE FIELD, YOU DO ME MISCHIEF.
YOUR WRONGS DO SET A SCANDAL ON MY SEX.
WE CANNOT FIGHT FOR LOVE, AS MEN MAY DO.

WE SHOULD BE WOOED AND WERE NOT MADE TO WOO.
I'LL FOLLOW THEE AND MAKE A HEAVEN OF HELL, TO DIE UPON THE HAND I LOVE SO WELL.
FARE THEE WELL, NYMPH.
ERE HE DO LEAVE THIS GROVE, HE SHALL SEEK THY LOVE.

HAST THOU THE FLOWER THERE?
AY, THERE IT IS.
I KNOW WHERE SLEEPS TITANIA THE NIGHT, LULLED IN FLOWERS WITH DANCES AND DELIGHT.
WITH THE JUICE OF THIS I'LL STREAK HER EYES AND MAKE HER FULL OF HATEFUL FANTASIES.

TAKE THOU SOME OF IT AND SEEK THROUGH THIS GROVE...
A SWEET LADY IS IN LOVE WITH A DISDAINFUL YOUTH.
ANOINT HIS EYES, BUT DO IT WHEN THE NEXT THING HE ESPIES MAY BE THE LADY.
NO LOVE.
LOVE?
LOVE!
LOVE! LOVE! LOVE!
THOU SHALT KNOW THE MAN BY THE ATHENIAN GARMENTS HE HATH ON.
MY LORD, YOUR SERVANT SHALL DO SO.

COME, NOW A ROUNDEL AND A FAIRY SONG.
KEEP BACK THE CLAMOROUS OWL THAT NIGHTLY HOOTS AND WONDERS AT OUR QUAINT SPIRITS.
SING ME NOW ASLEEP AND LET ME REST.

SNAKES, HEDGEHOGS
AND BLIND-WORMS,
COME NOT NEAR
OUR FAIRY QUEEN.
NEVER HARM NOR
SPELL NOR CHARM
COME OUR LOVELY
LADY NIGH.
SO GOOD NIGHT,
WITH LULLABY.
Z
Z
Z
HENCE, AWAY!
NOW ALL IS WELL.
ONE ALOOF
STAND SENTINEL.

ZZZZZ
WHAT THOU SEEST WHEN THOU DOST WAKE,
DO IT FOR THY TRUE LOVE TAKE.
LOVE AND LANGUISH FOR HIS SAKE.
WHEN THOU WAK'ST, IT IS THY DEAR.
WAKE WHEN SOME VILE THING IS NEAR!

SHUFF
SHUFF
SHUFF...
SHU...
SHUFF
SHU-
FAIR LOVE, YOU FAINT WITH WANDERING IN THE WOOD.
AND TO SPEAK TRUTH, I HAVE FORGOT OUR WAY.
WE'LL REST US, HERMIA.
LYSANDER, FIND YOU OUT A BED, FOR I UPON THIS BANK WILL REST MY HEAD.
ONE TURF SHALL SERVE AS PILLOW FOR US BOTH.
FOR MY SAKE, MY DEAR, DO NOT LIE SO NEAR.

MY HEART UNTO YOURS IS KNIT,
SO THAT BUT ONE HEART WE CAN MAKE OF IT.
THEN BY YOUR SIDE NO BEDROOM ME DENY,
FOR, LYING SO, HERMIA, I DO NOT LIE.
LYSANDER RIDDLES VERY PRETTILY.
BUT, GENTLE FRIEND, FOR LOVE AND COURTESY LIE FURTHER OFF, IN HUMAN MODESTY.

GOOD NIGHT, SWEET FRIEND.
THY LOVE NEVER ALTER
TILL THY SWEET LIFE END!
AMEN TO THAT
FAIR PRAYER, SAY I.
AND THEN END LIFE
WHEN I END LOYALTY!
HERE IS MY BED.
SLEEP GIVE THEE
ALL HIS REST!

WHO IS HERE?
WEEDS OF ATHENS HE DOTH WEAR.
THIS IS HE, MY MASTER SAID...
AND HERE THE MAIDEN ON THE DANK AND DIRTY GROUND.
SHE DURST NOT LIE NEAR THIS LACK-LOVE, THIS KILL-COURTESY.
1159

SQUEEE...
CHURL!
UPON THY EYES I THROW ALL THE POWER THIS CHARM DOTH OWE.
SQUEEZE
SQUEEZE
WHEN THOU WAK'ST, LET LOVE FORBID SLEEP ON THY EYELID.
SO AWAKE WHEN I AM GONE — FOR I MUST NOW TO OBERON.

STAY, THOUGH THOU KILL ME, SWEET DEMETRIUS!
DO NOT HAUNT ME THUS.
!
WHOOF
O!
Thud.
WILT THOU DARKLING LEAVE ME?
DO NOT SO.
STAY, ON THY PERIL.
I ALONE WILL GO.

O,
I AM OUT OF BREATH IN THIS FOND CHASE.
HAPPY IS HERMIA, FOR SHE HATH BLESSED AND ATTRACTIVE EYES.
I AM AS UGLY AS A BEAR — FOR BEASTS THAT MEET ME RUN AWAY FOR FEAR...

LYSANDER!
BUT WHO IS HERE?
DEAD OR ASLEEP?
LYSANDER, IF YOU LIVE, GOOD SIR, AWAKE.
AND RUN THROUGH FIRE I WILL FOR THY SWEET SAKE.
WHERE IS DEMETRIUS?
O, HOW FIT A WORD IS THAT VILE NAME TO PERISH ON MY SWORD!

DO NOT SAY SO, LYSANDER.
WHAT THOUGH HE LOVE YOUR HERMIA?
YET HERMIA STILL LOVES YOU.
THEN BE CONTENT.
CONTENT WITH HERMIA?
NO, I DO REPENT THE TEDIOUS MINUTES I WITH HER HAVE SPENT.
NOT HERMIA BUT HELENA I LOVE.
WHO WILL NOT CHANGE A RAVEN FOR A DOVE?

REASON SAYS YOU ARE THE WORTHIER MAID,
AND LEADS ME TO YOUR EYES WHERE I OVERLOOK...
LOVE'S STORIES WRITTEN IN LOVE'S RICHEST BOOK.
WHEREFORE WAS I TO THIS KEEN MOCKERY BORN?
WHEN AT YOUR HANDS DID I DESERVE THIS SCORN?
I NEVER CAN DESERVE A SWEET LOOK FROM DEMETRIUS' EYE...
BUT YOU MUST FLOUT MY INSUFFICIENCY?

YOU DO ME WRONG, BUT FARE YOU WELL.
I MUST CONFESS I THOUGHT YOU LORD OF MORE TRUE GENTLENESS.
O, THAT A LADY OF ONE MAN REFUSED
SHOULD OF ANOTHER THEREFORE BE ABUSED!
STOMP
STOMP
STOMP
SHE SEES NOT HERMIA.

HERMIA, SLEEP THOU THERE AND NEVER MAYST THOU COME LYSANDER NEAR.
FOR, AS A SURFEIT OF THE SWEETEST THINGS LOATHING TO THE STOMACH BRINGS...
SO THOU BE HATED!
ALL MY POWERS — ADDRESS YOUR LOVE AND MIGHT TO HONOUR HELEN,
AND BE HER KNIGHT.

METHOUGHT A SERPENT ATE MY HEART AWAY,
AND YOU SAT SMILING AT HIS CRUEL PREY.
HELP ME,
LYSANDER,
HELP ME!
LYSANDER!
GONE?
EITHER DEATH OR YOU I'LL FIND IMMEDIATELY.

PETER QUINCE –
THERE ARE THINGS IN THIS COMEDY THAT WILL NEVER PLEASE.
FIRST PYRAMUS MUST DRAW A SWORD TO KILL HIMSELF,
WHICH THE LADIES CANNOT ABIDE.
A PARLOUS FEAR.
I BELIEVE WE MUST LEAVE THE KILLING OUT.

I HAVE A DEVICE TO MAKE ALL WELL.
WRITE ME A PROLOGUE TO SAY WE WILL DO NO HARM WITH OUR SWORDS.
TELL THEM THAT I, PYRAMUS,
AM NOT PYRAMUS,
SHUFF
BUT BOTTOM THE WEAVER.
THIS WILL PUT THEM OUT OF FEAR.
WE WILL HAVE SUCH A PROLOGUE.

WILL NOT THE LADIES BE AFEARD OF THE LION?
I FEAR IT, I PROMISE YOU.
TO BRING IN A LION AMONG LADIES IS A MOST DREADFUL THING.
FOR THERE IS NOT A MORE FEARFUL WILD-FOWL THAN YOUR LION.
ANOTHER PROLOGUE MUST TELL HE IS NOT A LION.

NAY, NAME HIS NAME...
AND TELL THEM PLAINLY HE IS SNUG THE JOINER.
NOTE
?
BUT THERE IS TWO HARD THINGS –
TO BRING THE MOONLIGHT INTO A CHAMBER...
FOR PYRAMUS AND THISBE MEET BY MOONLIGHT.

BEEP! BEEP! BEEP!
DOTH THE MOON SHINE THAT NIGHT WE PLAY OUR PLAY?
YES, IT DOTH SHINE THAT NIGHT.
WHY, THEN MAY YOU LEAVE A WINDOW OPEN.

OR ELSE ONE MUST COME IN WITH A LANTERN AND
SAY HE COMES TO PRESENT THE PERSON OF MOONSHINE.
(LATE!)
THEN, THERE IS ANOTHER THING.
WE MUST HAVE A WALL, FOR PYRAMUS AND THISBE, SAYS THE STORY,
DID TALK THROUGH THE CHINK OF A WALL.
YOU CAN NEVER BRING IN A WALL.

SOME MAN OR OTHER MUST PRESENT "WALL".
LET HIM HOLD HIS FINGERS THUS,
AND THROUGH THAT CRANNY SHALL PYRAMUS AND THISBE WHISPER.
THEN ALL IS WELL.
COME, REHEARSE YOUR PARTS.
PYRAMUS, WHEN YOU HAVE SPOKEN YOUR SPEECH, ENTER INTO THAT BRAKE.
?

WHAT HAVE WE HERE, SO NEAR THE CRADLE OF THE FAIRY QUEEN?
WHAT! A PLAY?
I'LL BE AN AUDITOR – AN ACTOR TOO PERHAPS, IF I SEE CAUSE.
SPEAK, PYRAMUS – THISBE, STAND FORTH!

"THISBE, THE FLOWERS HAVE ODIOUS SAVOURS SWEET –"
ODOROUS! ODOROUS!
"– ODOURS SAVOURS SWEET."
"MY DEAREST THISBE DEAR, STAY THOU BUT HERE AWHILE,
AND BY AND BY I WILL TO THEE APPEAR."
A STRANGER PYRAMUS THAN EVER PLAYED HERE!

MUST I SPEAK NOW?
AY, HE GOES BUT TO SEE A NOISE THAT HE HEARD, AND IS TO COME AGAIN.
"MOST RADIANT PYRAMUS, MOST LILY-WHITE OF HUE... I'LL MEET THEE, PYRAMUS, AT NINNY'S TOMB."
NINUS' TOMB, MAN!
PYRAMUS, ENTER! YOUR CUE IS PAST.

"IF I WERE FAIR, FAIR THISBE..."
O MONSTROUS! O STRANGE! WE ARE HAUNTED!
WHY DO THEY RUN AWAY?

O BOTTOM, THOU ART CHANGED!
BLESS THEE, BOTTOM! THOU ART TRANSLATED.
RUN AWAY!!
I SEE THEIR KNAVERY. THIS IS TO MAKE AN ASS OF ME, TO FRIGHT ME, IF THEY COULD.
BUT I WILL NOT STIR FROM THIS PLACE, DO WHAT THEY CAN.

I WILL SING, THAT THEY SHALL HEAR I AM NOT AFRAID.
WHAT ANGEL WAKES ME FROM MY FLOWERY BED?
SO IS MINE EYE ENTHRALLED TO THY SHAPE,
ON THE FIRST VIEW, TO SAY, TO SWEAR...
?!
I LOVE THEE.

YOU SHOULD HAVE LITTLE REASON FOR THAT,
AND YET, TO SAY THE TRUTH,
REASON AND LOVE KEEP LITTLE COMPANY TOGETHER NOWADAYS.
THOU ART AS WISE AS THOU ART BEAUTIFUL.
ENOUGH TO GET OUT OF THIS WOOD.
SHUFFLE
OUT OF THIS WOOD DO NOT DESIRE TO GO!
THOU SHALT REMAIN HERE, WHETHER THOU WILT OR NO.

AND I DO LOVE THEE. THEREFORE, GO WITH ME.
I'LL GIVE THEE FAIRIES TO ATTEND ON THEE.
PEASEBLOSSOM!
SNAP!!
COBWEB!
MOTH!
AND MUSTARDSEED!

BE KIND AND COURTEOUS TO THIS GENTLEMAN.
FEED HIM WITH APRICOTS AND DEWBERRIES, PURPLE GRAPES, GREEN FIGS AND MULBERRIES.
HONEY-BAGS STEAL FROM THE HUMBLE-BEES.
AND PLUCK THE WINGS FROM PAINTED BUTTERFLIES TO FAN THE MOONBEAMS FROM HIS SLEEPING EYES.

LOVE!
HAIL!
HAIL, MORTAL!
HAIL!
HAIL!
I CRY YOUR WORSHIPS MERCY, HEARTILY.

COME, WAIT UPON HIM.
LEAD HIM TO MY BOWER.
THE MOON LOOKS WITH A WATERY EYE, AND WHEN SHE WEEPS,
WEEPS EVERY LITTLE FLOWER, LAMENTING SOME ENFORCED CHASTITY.
TIE UP MY LOVE'S TONGUE, BRING HIM SILENTLY.

I WONDER IF TITANIA BE AWAKED...
THEN WHAT NEXT CAME IN HER EYE, WHICH SHE MUST DOTE ON IN EXTREMITY.
HERE COMES MY MESSENGER.
HOW NOW, MAD SPIRIT!
WHAT NIGHT-RULE NOW ABOUT THIS HAUNTED GROVE?
MY MISTRESS WITH A **MONSTER** IS IN LOVE.

NEAR TO HER CONSECRATED BOWER,
WHILE SHE WAS IN HER SLEEPING HOUR,
A CREW OF RUDE MECHANICALS WERE MET TOGETHER
TO REHEARSE A PLAY INTENDED FOR GREAT THESEUS' NUPTIAL DAY.

PYRAMUS FORSOOK HIS SCENE AND I DID HIM AT THIS ADVANTAGE TAKE...
AN ASS'S NOLE I FIXED ON HIS HEAD –
AND **FORTH** MY MIMIC COMES.

WHEN THEY HIM SPY,
AS WILD GEESE RISING AND CAWING AT THE GUN'S REPORT,
SO, AT HIS SIGHT...
AWAY HIS FELLOWS FLY.
BRIERS AND THORNS AT THEIR APPAREL SNATCH.

I LED THEM ON IN
THIS DISTRACTED FEAR...
AND LEFT SWEET PYRAMUS
TRANSLATED THERE.

FLICK!
WHEN IN THAT MOMENT,
SO IT CAME TO PASS,
FLICK!
TITANIA WAKED AND
STRAIGHTWAY LOVED AN ASS.
PFFFT!
THIS FALLS OUT BETTER
THAN I COULD DEVISE.

BUT HAST THOU YET LATCHED THE ATHENIAN'S EYES WITH THE LOVE-JUICE, AS I DID BID THEE DO?
YOINK
I TOOK HIM SLEEPING – THAT IS FINISHED TOO.
AND THE ATHENIAN WOMAN BY HIS SIDE, WHEN HE WAKED, OF FORCE SHE MUST BE EYED.
?
BIF!

STAND CLOSE: THIS IS THE SAME ATHENIAN.
THIS IS THE WOMAN, BUT NOT THIS THE MAN.
O, WHY REBUKE YOU HIM THAT LOVES YOU SO?
THOU, I FEAR, HAST GIVEN ME CAUSE TO CURSE.

KRIIII..
IF THOU HAST SLAIN LYSANDER IN HIS SLEEP, KILL ME TOO.
SNAP
WOULD HE HAVE STOLEN AWAY FROM SLEEPING HERMIA?
IT CANNOT BE BUT THOU HAST MURDERED HIM.

RUB RUB
SO SHOULD A MURDERER LOOK, SO DEAD, SO GRIM.
TCH!
SO SHOULD THE MURDERED LOOK,
PIERCED THROUGH THE HEART WITH YOUR STERN CRUELTY.
POIK!
YET YOU, THE MURDERER, LOOK AS BRIGHT AS YONDER VENUS IN HER GLIMMERING SPHERE.
WHAT'S THIS TO MY LYSANDER? WHERE IS HE?

AH, GOOD DEMETRIUS, WILT THOU GIVE HIM ME?
I HAD RATHER GIVE HIS CARCASS TO MY HOUNDS.
STOMP
OUT, DOG! HAST THOU SLAIN HIM THEN?
O, ONCE TELL TRUE, EVEN FOR MY SAKE –
HAST THOU KILLED HIM SLEEPING?

I AM NOT GUILTY OF LYSANDER'S BLOOD.
NOR IS HE DEAD,
FOR AUGHT THAT I CAN TELL.
I PRAY THEE, TELL ME THEN THAT HE IS WELL.
WHAT SHOULD I GET THERE-FOR?
A PRIVILEGE NEVER TO SEE ME MORE,
WHETHER HE BE DEAD OR NO.
CRUNCH
CRUNCH
SNAP

THERE IS NO FOLLOWING HER IN THIS FIERCE VEIN.
HERE THEREFORE FOR A WHILE I WILL REMAIN.
SORROW'S HEAVINESS DOTH HEAVIER GROW...
WHAT HAST THOU DONE?

THOU HAST MISTAKEN QUITE, AND LAID THE LOVE-JUICE ON SOME TRUE LOVE'S SIGHT.
THEN FATE OVERRULES.
Gyuuu....
ABOUT THE WOOD GO SWIFTER THAN THE WIND...

SQUISH
SQUISH
HELENA OF ATHENS LOOK THOU FIND.
ALL FANCY-SICK SHE IS AND PALE OF CHEER WITH SIGHS OF LOVE.
SQUIIII...
BY SOME ILLUSION SEE THOU BRING HER HERE.
I'LL CHARM HIS EYES AGAIN.
I GO, LOOK HOW I GO, SWIFTER THAN ARROW FROM THE TARTAR'S BOW.

SNORK
FLOWER OF THIS PURPLE DYE, WHEN HIS LOVE HE DOTH ESPY,
LET HER SHINE AS GLORIOUSLY AS THE VENUS OF THE SKY.
WHEN THOU WAKEST, IF SHE BE BY, BEG OF HER FOR REMEDY.

CAPTAIN OF OUR FAIRY BAND,
POP!
HELENA IS HERE AT HAND —
AND THE YOUTH MISTOOK BY ME.
SHALL WE THEIR FOND PAGEANT SEE?
LORD, WHAT FOOLS THESE MORTALS BE!

THE NOISE THEY MAKE WILL CAUSE DEMETRIUS TO AWAKE.
THEN WILL TWO AT ONCE WOO ONE.
THOSE THINGS DO BEST PLEASE ME THAT BEFALL PREPOSTEROUSLY.

WHY SHOULD YOU THINK THAT I SHOULD WOO IN SCORN?
SCORN AND DERISION NEVER COME IN TEARS.
HOW CAN THESE THINGS IN ME SEEM SCORN TO YOU...
BEARING THE BADGE OF FAITH TO PROVE THEM TRUE?
SNIF SNIF
YOU DO ADVANCE YOUR CUNNING MORE AND MORE, WHEN TRUTH KILLS TRUTH.
THESE VOWS ARE HERMIA'S. WILL YOU GIVE HER O'ER?

I HAD NO JUDGEMENT WHEN TO HER I SWORE.
NOR NONE IN MY MIND NOW YOU GIVE HER O'ER.
DEMETRIUS LOVES HER AND LOVES NOT YOU.
Z
!
BLINK!
O HELEN!
GODDESS,
NYMPH,
PERFECT,
DIVINE!
TO WHAT, MY LOVE, SHALL I COMPARE THINE EYNE?

THY LIPS, THOSE KISSING CHERRIES...
THAT PURE CONGEALED WHITE.
O, LET ME KISS THIS PRINCESS OF PURE WHITE...
THIS SEAL OF BLISS!
O SPITE!
O HELL!
?
I SEE YOU ALL ARE BENT TO SET AGAINST ME FOR YOUR MERRIMENT.

IF YOU WERE MEN,
YOU WOULD NOT USE A GENTLE LADY SO —
TO VOW, AND SUPERPRAISE MY PARTS.
YOU BOTH ARE RIVALS, AND LOVE HERMIA,
AND NOW BOTH RIVALS TO MOCK HELENA.

CHEW! CHEW! CHEW!
YOU ARE UNKIND, DEMETRIUS.
BE NOT SO, FOR YOU LOVE HERMIA: THIS YOU KNOW I KNOW.
SMACK!!
!
WITH ALL MY HEART, IN HERMIA'S LOVE I YIELD YOU UP MY PART.
AND YOURS OF HELENA TO ME BEQUEATH, WHOM I DO LOVE AND WILL DO TO MY DEATH.
NEVER DID MOCKERS WASTE MORE IDLE BREATH.

LYSANDER, KEEP THY HERMIA. I WILL NONE.
SMAK!!
MY HEART NOW TO HELEN IS HOME RETURNED, THERE TO REMAIN.
HELEN, IT IS NOT SO.
LOOK WHERE THY LOVE COMES...
YONDER IS THY DEAR.

LYSANDER, WHY UNKINDLY DIDST THOU LEAVE ME SO?
WHY SHOULD HE STAY WHOM LOVE DOTH PRESS TO GO?
WHAT LOVE COULD PRESS LYSANDER FROM MY SIDE?

WHY SEEKEST THOU ME?
COULD NOT THIS MAKE THEE KNOW THE HATE I BEAR THEE MADE ME LEAVE THEE SO?
YOU SPEAK NOT AS YOU THINK.
IT CANNOT BE.
NOW I PERCEIVE THEY HAVE CONJOINED ALL THREE TO FASHION THIS FALSE SPORT IN SPITE OF ME!

THE SISTERS' VOWS, THE HOURS THAT WE HAVE SPENT—
O, IS ALL FORGOT?
WILL YOU REND OUR ANCIENT LOVE ASUNDER TO JOIN WITH MEN IN SCORNING YOUR POOR FRIEND?
I AM AMAZED AT YOUR PASSIONATE WORDS.
I SCORN YOU NOT. IT SEEMS THAT YOU SCORN ME.

HAVE YOU NOT SET LYSANDER TO FOLLOW ME AND PRAISE MY EYES AND FACE?

AND MADE YOUR OTHER LOVE, DEMETRIUS, TO CALL ME GODDESS?

WHEREFORE DOTH LYSANDER DENY YOUR LOVE BUT BY ***YOUR*** CONSENT?

I UNDERSTAND NOT WHAT YOU MEAN BY THIS.

AY, COUNTERFEIT SAD LOOKS.
WHEN I TURN MY BACK, **WINK** EACH AT OTHER.
BUT FARE YE WELL:
'TIS PARTLY MINE OWN FAULT...
WHICH DEATH OR ABSENCE SOON SHALL REMEDY.
BRUSH
BRUSH
BRUSH
SCUFFLE!
SHOVE!

HELEN, I LOVE THEE, BY MY LIFE I DO!
I SAY I LOVE THEE MORE THAN HE CAN DO!
LYSANDER, WHERETO TENDS ALL THIS?
AWAY...
YOU ETHIOPE!

WHAT CHANGE IS THIS, SWEET LOVE?
THY **LOVE**? OUT, TAWNY TARTAR, **OUT**! HATED POISON, **HENCE**!
DO YOU NOT JEST?
AM NOT I HERMIA? ARE NOT YOU LYSANDER?
BE CERTAIN, NOTHING TRUER: 'TIS NO JEST THAT I DO **HATE** THEE AND LOVE **HELENA**.

WHAT! HAVE YOU COME BY NIGHT AND STOLEN MY LOVE'S HEART FROM HIM?
YOU THIEF OF LOVE!
FIE, FIE! YOU COUNTERFEIT, YOU PUPPET YOU!
PUPPET! WHY SO?
ARE YOU GROWN SO HIGH IN HIS ESTEEM BECAUSE I AM SO DWARFISH AND SO LOW?

HOW LOW AM I, THOU PAINTED MAYPOLE?
NOT YET SO LOW BUT THAT MY NAILS CAN REACH UNTO THINE EYES!
LET HER NOT HURT ME.
I AM A RIGHT MAID FOR MY COWARDICE.
YOU PERHAPS MAY THINK, BECAUSE SHE IS SOMETHING LOWER THAN MYSELF, THAT I CAN MATCH HER.
"LOWER"! HARK, AGAIN!

BE NOT AFRAID. SHE SHALL NOT HARM THEE, HELENA.
NO, SIR. SHE SHALL NOT, THOUGH YOU TAKE HER PART.
SSSQUAK!
O, WHEN SHE'S ANGRY, THOUGH SHE BE BUT LITTLE, SHE IS FIERCE!
"LITTLE" AGAIN! NOTHING BUT "LOW" AND "LITTLE"!
THWACK!

WHY WILL YOU SUFFER HER TO FLOUT ME THUS? **LET ME COME TO HER.**

GET YOU GONE, YOU **DWARF**, YOU **MINIMUS**, YOU **BEAD**, YOU **ACORN**!

YOU ARE TOO OFFICIOUS IN HER BEHALF THAT SCORNS YOUR SERVICES.

NOW FOLLOW, IF THOU DAREST, TO TRY WHOSE RIGHT, THINE OR MINE, IS MOST IN HELENA.
FOLLOW?
NAY, I'LL GO WITH THEE, CHEEK BY JOWL.
YOUR HANDS THAN MINE ARE QUICKER FOR A FRAY...
MY LEGS ARE LONGER THOUGH TO RUN AWAY.
I AM AMAZED AND KNOW NOT WHAT TO SAY.

THIS IS **THY** NEGLIGENCE.
STILL THOU MISTAKE... OR ELSE COMMIT THY KNAVERIES WILFULLY.
BELIEVE ME, KING OF SHADOWS, I MISTOOK.
THESE LOVERS SEEK A PLACE TO FIGHT.
HIE THEREFORE, ROBIN, OVERCAST THE NIGHT...
LEAD THESE TESTY RIVALS SO ASTRAY, AS ONE COME NOT WITHIN ANOTHER'S WAY.

LEAD THEM THUS,
TILL OVER THEIR BROWS SLEEP, WITH LEADEN LEGS...
AND BATTY WINGS, DOTH CREEP.
THEN CRUSH THIS HERB INTO LYSANDER'S EYE.
LYSANDER!
LYSANDER!
WHEN THEY NEXT WAKE,
ALL THIS DERISION SHALL SEEM A DREAM AND FRUITLESS VISION.

I'LL TO MY QUEEN AND HER EYE RELEASE FROM MONSTER'S VIEW –
- ACQUIRE BOY
- DRUG QUEEN
- MOCK QUEEN
- ACQUIRE BOY
AND ALL THINGS SHALL BE PEACE.
MY FAIRY LORD, THIS MUST BE DONE WITH HASTE...
FOR YONDER SHINES AURORA'S HARBINGER AT WHOSE APPROACH...
LYSANDER!
GHOSTS, WANDERING HERE AND THERE,
TROOP HOME TO CHURCHYARDS.

BUT WE ARE SPIRITS OF ANOTHER SORT.
I WITH THE MORNING'S LOVE HAVE OFT MADE SPORT,
EVEN TILL THE EASTERN GATE
TURNS INTO YELLOW GOLD.
BUT **HASTE,** MAKE NO DELAY.
WE MAY EFFECT THIS BUSINESS YET ERE DAY.

STAMP
STAMP
I AM FEARED IN FIELD AND TOWN.
STAMP
STAMP
STOP!
GOBLIN, LEAD THEM UP AND DOWN.
HERE COMES ONE.
WHERE ART THOU, PROUD DEMETRIUS?
SPEAK THOU NOW.
"HERE, VILLAIN! DRAWN AND READY. WHERE ART THOU?"
?
THE VILLAIN IS MUCH LIGHTER-HEELED THAN I.
I FOLLOWED FAST, BUT FASTER HE DID FLY...
FALLEN AM I IN DARK UNEVEN WAY, AND HERE WILL REST ME.

THOU RUNN'ST BEFORE ME AND DAR'ST NOT STAND NOR LOOK ME IN THE FACE.
WHERE ART THOU NOW?
"COME HITHER. I AM HERE."
THOU SHALT BUY THIS DEAR IF EVER I THY FACE BY DAYLIGHT SEE.
NOW, GO THY WAY.
FAINTNESS CONSTRAINETH ME TO MEASURE OUT MY LENGTH ON THIS COLD BED.

O WEARY NIGHT!
SHINE FROM THE EAST THAT I MAY BACK TO ATHENS BY DAYLIGHT.
SLEEP, THAT SOMETIMES SHUTS UP SORROW'S EYE, STEAL ME A WHILE FROM MINE OWN COMPANY.
YET BUT THREE?
HERE SHE COMES.
CUPID IS A KNAVISH LAD
THUS TO MAKE POOR FEMALES MAD.

NEVER SO WEARY, I CAN NO FURTHER CRAWL.
HERE WILL I REST ME TILL THE BREAK OF DAY.
LYSANDER
GENTLE LOVER, REMEDY...
THOU TAK'ST TRUE DELIGHT IN THE SIGHT OF THY **FORMER** LADY'S EYE.
JACK SHALL HAVE JILL, NAUGHT SHALL GO ILL
AND ALL SHALL BE WELL.

COME, SIT THEE DOWN UPON THIS FLOWERY BED
WHILE I KISS THY FAIR LARGE EARS, MY GENTLE JOY.
WILT THOU HEAR SOME MUSIC, MY **SWEET** LOVE?
TWITCH
I HAVE A REASONABLE GOOD EAR IN MUSIC.
LET US HAVE THE TONGS AND THE BONES.
!

OR SAY, SWEET LOVE, WHAT THOU DESIREST TO EAT.
TRULY, I COULD MUNCH YOUR GOOD DRY OATS.
I HAVE A GREAT DESIRE TO A BOTTLE OF GOOD HAY, SWEET HAY...
BUT, I PRAY YOU, LET NONE OF YOUR PEOPLE STIR ME.
I HAVE AN EXPOSITION OF SLEEP COME UPON ME.

SLEEP THOU, AND I WILL WIND THEE IN MY ARMS.
FAIRIES, BE GONE!
Zz
O, HOW I LOVE THEE!
Zz
HOW I DOTE ON THEE!
WELCOME, GOOD ROBIN.
SEEST THOU THIS SWEET SIGHT?
HER DOTAGE NOW I DO BEGIN TO PITY.

FOR, MEETING HER OF LATE,
I THEN DID ASK OF HER
HER CHANGELING CHILD, WHICH
STRAIGHT SHE GAVE ME.

NOW, MY TITANIA,
WAKE YOU, MY SWEET QUEEN.
MY OBERON!
WHAT VISIONS HAVE I SEEN!
METHOUGHT I WAS ENAMOURED OF AN ASS.
THERE LIES YOUR LOVE.
SCRATCH
SCRATCH
HOW CAME THESE THINGS TO PASS?

ROBIN, TAKE OFF THIS HEAD.
TUG!
TITANIA, MUSIC CALL.
MUSIC, HO! MUSIC SUCH AS CHARMETH SLEEP.
COME, MY QUEEN, TAKE HANDS WITH ME...
AND ROCK THE GROUND WHEREON THESE SLEEPERS BE.

NOW THOU AND I WILL TOMORROW MIDNIGHT...
SOLEMNLY DANCE IN DUKE THESEUS' HOUSE TRIUMPHANTLY.
THERE SHALL THE PAIRS OF FAITHFUL LOVERS BE WEDDED, WITH THESEUS, ALL IN JOLLITY.

FAIRY KING, ATTEND AND MARK — I DO HEAR THE MORNING LARK.
THEN, MY QUEEN, TRIP WE AFTER THE NIGHT'S SHADE.
WE THE GLOBE CAN COMPASS SOON, SWIFTER THAN THE WANDERING MOON.
COME, MY LORD, AND TELL ME HOW IT CAME THAT I SLEEPING HERE WAS FOUND WITH THESE MORTALS ON THE GROUND.
DRUG,
MOCK

MY LOVE SHALL HEAR THE MUSIC OF MY HOUNDS.
UNCOUPLE IN THE WESTERN VALLEY — LET THEM GO!
WE WILL, FAIR QUEEN, UP TO THE MOUNTAIN'S TOP AND MARK THE MUSICAL CONFUSION OF HOUNDS.

I WAS WITH HERCULES AND CADMUS ONCE,
WHEN IN A WOOD OF CRETE THEY BAYED THE BEAR WITH HOUNDS OF SPARTA.
I NEVER HEARD SO MUSICAL A DISCORD, SUCH SWEET THUNDER.

MY HOUNDS ARE BRED OUT OF THE SPARTAN KIND...
WITH EARS THAT SWEEP AWAY THE MORNING DEW.
CROOK-KNEE'D AND DEWLAPPED LIKE THESSALIAN BULLS...
SLOW IN PURSUIT BUT MATCHED IN MOUTH LIKE BELLS.

BUT SOFT!
WHAT NYMPHS ARE THESE?
?
MY LORD, THIS IS MY DAUGHTER HERE ASLEEP...
AND THIS LYSANDER,
THIS DEMETRIUS IS,
THIS HELENA.
I WONDER OF THEIR BEING HERE TOGETHER.

NO DOUBT THEY ROSE UP EARLY TO OBSERVE THE RITE OF MAY
AND CAME HERE IN GRACE OF OUR SOLEMNITY.
BUT SPEAK, EGEUS, IS NOT THIS THE DAY THAT HERMIA SHOULD GIVE ANSWER OF HER CHOICE?
IT IS, MY LORD.
GO, BID THE HUNTSMEN WAKE THEM WITH THEIR HORNS.

BWAAAAAAAAAHH....
GOOD MORROW, FRIENDS. SAINT VALENTINE IS PAST.
BEGIN THESE WOOD-BIRDS BUT TO COUPLE NOW?
PARDON, MY LORD.
I KNOW YOU TWO ARE RIVAL ENEMIES.
HOW COMES THIS GENTLE CONCORD – TO SLEEP BY HATE AND FEAR NO ENMITY?
MY LORD, I SHALL REPLY AMAZEDLY,
HALF SLEEP, HALF WAKING.

I SWEAR I CANNOT TRULY SAY HOW I CAME HERE.
BUT I THINK I CAME WITH HERMIA HITHER.
OUR INTENT WAS TO BE GONE FROM ATHENS,
WHERE WE MIGHT WITHOUT THE PERIL OF THE ATHENIAN LAW...
ENOUGH!
MY LORD, YOU HAVE ENOUGH!

I BEG THE LAW UPON HIS HEAD.
THEY WOULD HAVE STOLEN AWAY, THEREBY TO HAVE **DEFEATED** YOU AND ME.
!
MY LORD, FAIR HELEN TOLD ME OF THEIR PURPOSE, AND I IN FURY HITHER FOLLOWED THEM...
HELENA FOLLOWING ME.

BUT, MY GOOD LORD...
BY SOME POWER...
MY LOVE TO HERMIA MELTED AS THE SNOW.
THE OBJECT AND THE PLEASURE OF MINE EYE IS ONLY HELENA.
SCUFF SCUFF
TO HER, MY LORD, WAS I BETROTHED AND WILL FOR EVERMORE BE TRUE.

FAIR LOVERS, YOU ARE FORTUNATELY MET.
EGEUS, I WILL OVERBEAR YOUR WILL.
FOR IN THE TEMPLE, BY AND BY WITH US, THESE COUPLES SHALL ETERNALLY BE KNIT.
AWAY WITH US TO ATHENS. THREE AND THREE, WE'LL HOLD A FEAST IN GREAT SOLEMNITY.

THESE THINGS SEEM SMALL AND UNDISTINGUISHABLE
LIKE FAR-OFF MOUNTAINS TURNED INTO CLOUDS.
EVERYTHING SEEMS DOUBLE.
AND I HAVE FOUND DEMETRIUS LIKE A JEWEL, MINE OWN, AND NOT MINE OWN.

ARE YOU SURE THAT WE ARE AWAKE?
STRETCH!
DO YOU NOT THINK THE DUKE WAS HERE AND BID US FOLLOW HIM?
YEA, AND MY FATHER.
WHY THEN WE **ARE** AWAKE.
LET'S FOLLOW HIM, AND BY THE WAY LET US RECOUNT OUR DREAMS.

ZZZ
ZZ
HEIGH-HO!
PETER QUINCE!
FLUTE, THE BELLOWS-MENDER!
SNOUT, THE TINKER!
STARVELING!
GOD'S MY LIFE!
STOLEN HENCE AND LEFT ME ASLEEP!
I HAVE HAD...
A MOST RARE VISION.
MAN IS BUT AN ASS IF HE GO ABOUT TO EXPOUND THIS DREAM.
PAT
PAT

THE EYE OF MAN HATH NOT HEARD,
THE EAR OF MAN HATH NOT SEEN,
?
MAN'S HAND IS NOT ABLE TO TASTE,
HIS TONGUE TO CONCEIVE, NOR HIS HEART TO REPORT...
WHAT MY DREAM WAS.
!
I WILL GET PETER QUINCE TO WRITE A BALLAD OF THIS DREAM.
IT SHALL BE CALLED..
"BOTTOM'S DREAM"
BECAUSE...
IT HATH NO BOTTOM.

HAVE YOU SENT TO BOTTOM'S HOUSE? IS HE COME HOME YET?
HE CANNOT BE HEARD OF.
IF HE COME NOT, THEN THE PLAY IS MARRED. IT GOES NOT FORWARD.
YOU HAVE NOT A MAN IN ALL ATHENS ABLE TO DISCHARGE PYRAMUS BUT HE.
THIS WAY UP
MASTERS, THE DUKE IS COMING FROM THE TEMPLE,
AND THERE IS TWO OR THREE LORDS AND LADIES MORE MARRIED.

WHERE ARE THESE LADS?
JOG!
JOG!
JOG!
BOTTOM! O, MOST HAPPY HOUR!
MASTERS, I AM TO DISCOURSE WONDERS.
BUT NOT A WORD OF ME. ALL THAT I WILL TELL YOU IS —
GET YOUR APPAREL TOGETHER, FOR OUR PLAY IS PREFERRED.
AND, MOST DEAR ACTORS, EAT NO ONIONS NOR GARLIC, FOR WE ARE TO UTTER SWEET BREATH.
NO MORE WORDS. AWAY!

'TIS STRANGE, MY THESEUS, THAT THESE LOVERS SPEAK OF.
MORE STRANGE THAN TRUE.
THE LUNATIC, THE LOVER AND THE POET ARE OF IMAGINATION ALL COMPACT.

IMAGINATION BODIES FORTH THE FORMS OF THINGS UNKNOWN...
AND GIVES TO AIRY NOTHING A LOCAL HABITATION AND A NAME.
!
SUCH TRICKS HATH STRONG IMAGINATION —
IN THE NIGHT, IMAGINING SOME FEAR, HOW EASY IS A **BUSH** SUPPOSED A **BEAR**!

BUT ALL THE STORY OF THE NIGHT TOLD OVER, AND ALL THEIR MINDS TRANSFIGURED SO TOGETHER,
GROWS TO SOMETHING OF GREAT CONSTANCY, HOWSOEVER STRANGE AND ADMIRABLE.
HERE COME THE LOVERS, FULL OF JOY AND MIRTH.

JOY, GENTLE FRIENDS!
FRESH DAYS OF LOVE ACCOMPANY YOUR HEARTS!
COME NOW, WHAT MASQUES, WHAT DANCES SHALL WE HAVE TO WEAR AWAY THIS LONG AGE OF THREE HOURS BETWEEN OUR AFTER-SUPPER AND BED-TIME?
WHAT REVELS ARE IN HAND?
CALL PHILOSTRATE.

HERE, MIGHTY THESEUS.
SAY, WHAT HAVE YOU FOR THIS EVENING?
HOW SHALL WE BEGUILE THE LAZY TIME, IF NOT WITH SOME DELIGHT?
MANY SPORTS ARE RIPE. MAKE CHOICE OF WHICH YOUR HIGHNESS WILL SEE FIRST.
"THE BATTLE WITH THE CENTAURS, TO BE SUNG BY AN ATHENIAN EUNUCH TO THE HARP."
WE'LL NONE OF THAT.

"THE RIOT OF THE TIPSY BACCHANALS, TEARING THE THRACIAN SINGER IN THEIR RAGE."
THAT IS AN OLD DEVICE PLAYED WHEN I FROM THEBES CAME LAST A CONQUEROR.
"THE THRICE THREE MUSES MOURNING FOR THE DEATH OF LEARNING, LATE DECEASED IN BEGGARY."
THAT IS SOME SATIRE, KEEN AND CRITICAL, NOT SORTING WITH A NUPTIAL CEREMONY.

"A TEDIOUS BRIEF SCENE
OF YOUNG PYRAMUS
AND HIS LOVE THISBE,
VERY TRAGICAL MIRTH."

!
MERRY AND TRAGICAL! TEDIOUS AND BRIEF!
THAT IS HOT ICE AND WONDROUS STRANGE SNOW.
HOW SHALL WE FIND THE CONCORD OF THIS DISCORD?
A PLAY THERE IS, MY LORD, SOME TEN WORDS LONG, WHICH IS AS "BRIEF" AS I HAVE KNOWN A PLAY –
BUT BY TEN WORDS, MY LORD, IT IS TOO LONG, WHICH MAKES IT TEDIOUS.

IN ALL THE PLAY THERE IS NOT ONE WORD APT, ONE PLAYER FITTED.
AND "TRAGICAL", MY NOBLE LORD, IT IS, FOR PYRAMUS THEREIN DOTH KILL HIMSELF...
WHICH WHEN I SAW REHEARSED, I MUST CONFESS, MADE MINE EYES WATER.
BUT MORE MERRY TEARS THE PASSION OF LOUD LAUGHTER NEVER SHED.

WHAT ARE THEY THAT DO PLAY IT?
HARD-HANDED MEN THAT WORK IN ATHENS HERE, WHICH NEVER LABOURED IN THEIR MINDS TILL NOW.
WE WILL HEAR IT.
NO, MY NOBLE LORD, IT IS NOT FOR YOU.
UNLESS YOU CAN FIND SPORT IN THEIR CRUEL PAIN TO DO YOU SERVICE.

I WILL HEAR THAT PLAY.
FOR NEVER ANYTHING CAN BE AMISS WHEN SIMPLENESS AND DUTY TENDER IT.
GO, BRING THEM IN.
I LOVE NOT TO SEE WRETCHEDNESS OVER-CHARGED.
WHY, GENTLE SWEET, YOU SHALL SEE **NO** SUCH THING.
HE SAYS THEY CAN DO **NOTHING** IN THIS KIND.

THE KINDER WE TO GIVE THEM THANKS FOR NOTHING.
TRUST ME, SWEET. OUT OF THIS SILENCE YET I PICKED A WELCOME.
IN THE MODESTY OF FEARFUL DUTY I READ AS MUCH AS FROM THE RATTLING TONGUE OF SAUCY AND AUDACIOUS ELOQUENCE.
LOVE AND TONGUE-TIED SIMPLICITY SPEAK MOST TO MY CAPACITY.

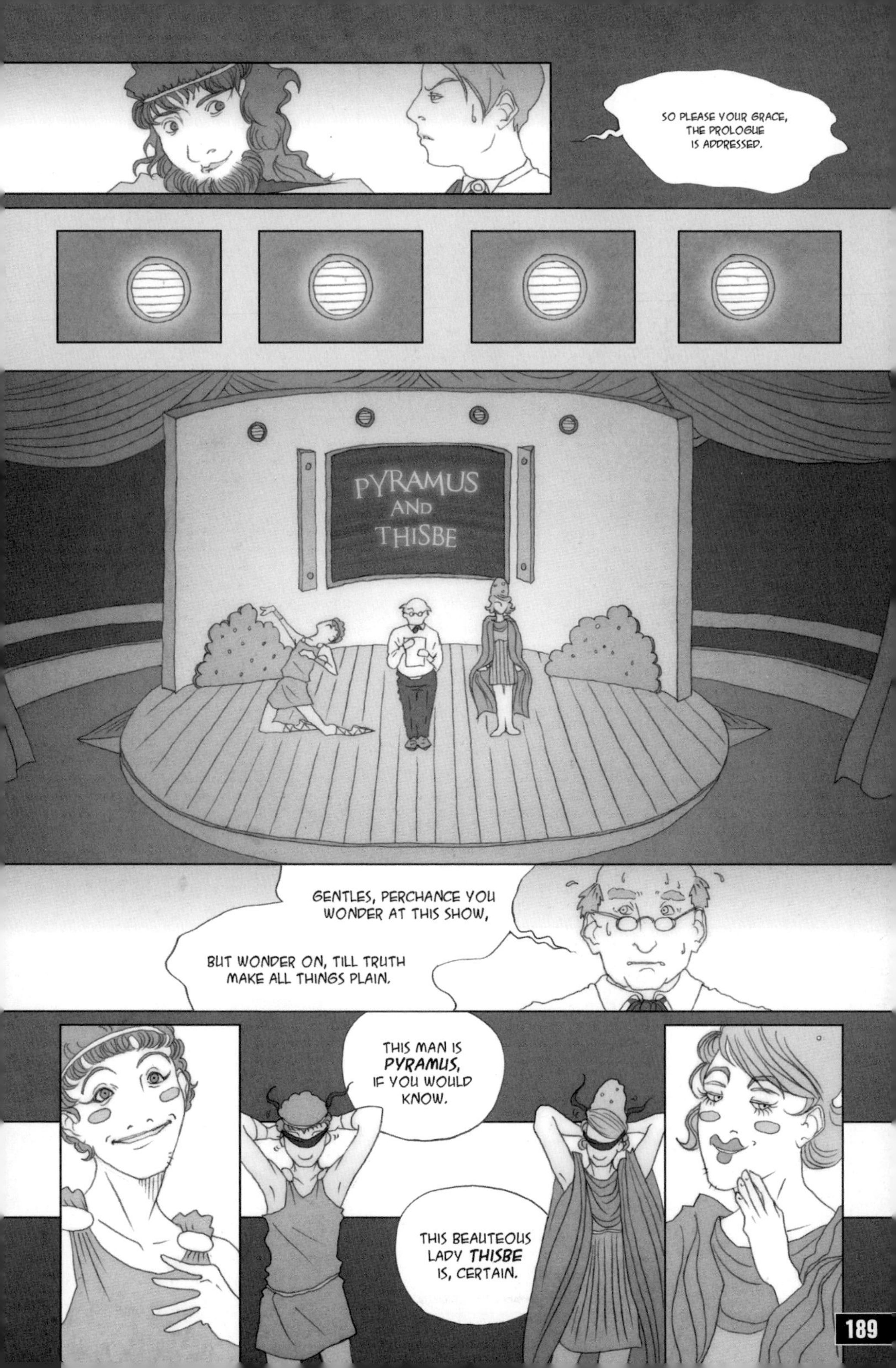
SO PLEASE YOUR GRACE, THE PROLOGUE IS ADDRESSED.
PYRAMUS AND THISBE
GENTLES, PERCHANCE YOU WONDER AT THIS SHOW,
BUT WONDER ON, TILL TRUTH MAKE ALL THINGS PLAIN.
THIS MAN IS PYRAMUS, IF YOU WOULD KNOW.
THIS BEAUTEOUS LADY THISBE IS, CERTAIN.

THIS MAN, WITH LIME AND ROUGH-CAST, DOTH PRESENT **WALL** –
THAT **VILE WALL** WHICH DID THESE LOVERS SUNDER.
AND THROUGH WALL'S CHINK, POOR SOULS,
THEY ARE CONTENT TO WHISPER.
THIS MAN, WITH LANTERN, DOG AND BUSH OF THORN, PRESENTETH **MOONSHINE.**
OW!
FOR, IF YOU WILL KNOW, BY MOONSHINE DID THESE LOVERS THINK NO SCORN TO MEET AT NINUS' TOMB, THERE TO WOO.

THIS GRISLY BEAST,
WHICH LION HIGHT BY NAME,
RAH
NINUS' TOOM
THE TRUSTY THISBE, COMING FIRST BY NIGHT,
RAH
DID SCARE AWAY.
AND, AS SHE FLED,
HER MANTLE SHE DID FALL,
RAH RAH RAH
Scream!
Rah.
WHICH LION VILE WITH BLOODY MOUTH DID STAIN.

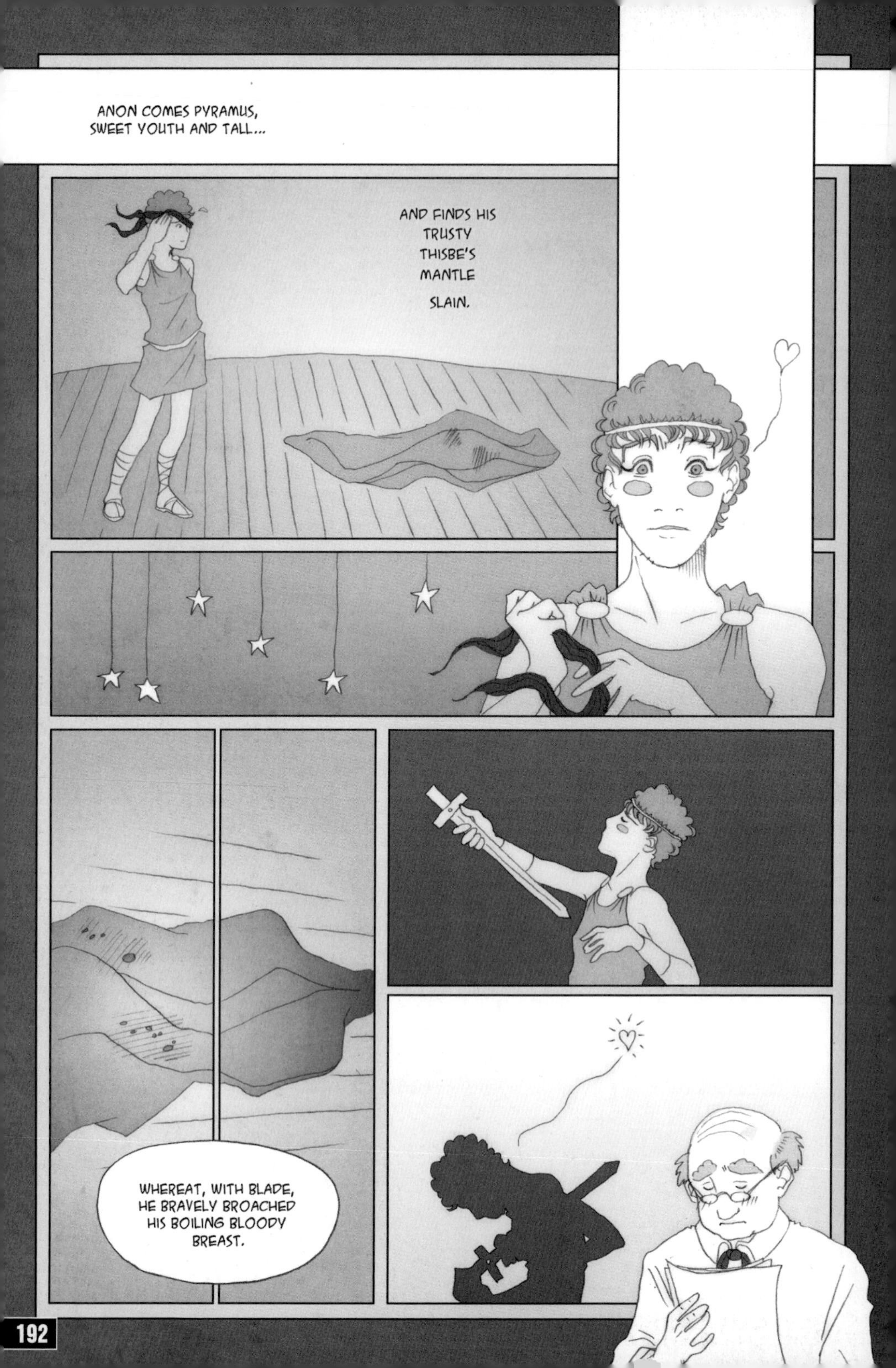
ANON COMES PYRAMUS,
SWEET YOUTH AND TALL...
AND FINDS HIS TRUSTY THISBE'S MANTLE SLAIN.
WHEREAT, WITH BLADE, HE BRAVELY BROACHED HIS BOILING BLOODY BREAST.

AND THISBE,
TARRYING IN MULBERRY SHADE...

CLAP...
...
THIS IS THE **SILLIEST** STUFF THAT EVER I HEARD.
THE BEST IN THIS KIND ARE BUT SHADOWS...
AND THE WORST ARE NO WORSE, IF IMAGINATION AMEND THEM.
MOONSHINE AND LION ARE LEFT TO BURY THE DEAD.
AY, AND WALL TOO.

NO, I ASSURE YOU,
THE WALL IS DOWN THAT PARTED THEIR FATHERS.
WILL IT PLEASE YOU TO SEE THE EPILOGUE?
NO EPILOGUE, I PRAY YOU, FOR YOUR PLAY NEEDS NO EXCUSE.
FOR WHEN THE PLAYERS ARE ALL DEAD, THERE NEED NONE TO BE BLAMED.
A FINE TRAGEDY, TRULY AND VERY NOTABLY DISCHARGED.
BUT COME, YOUR BERGOMASK ...

KIN-KANG
KIN-KANG
KIN-KANG
KIN-KANG
KIN-KANG
KIN-KANG
THE IRON TONGUE OF MIDNIGHT HATH TOLD TWELVE.
KIN-KANG
LOVERS, TO BED, 'TIS ALMOST FAIRY TIME.
KIN-KANG
KIN-KANG
I FEAR WE SHALL OUTSLEEP THE COMING MORN.
KIN-KANG
KIN-KANG
SWEET FRIENDS, A FORTNIGHT HOLD WE THIS SOLEMNITY IN NIGHTLY REVELS AND NEW JOLLITY.
KIN-KANG

NOW IT IS THE TIME OF NIGHT
THAT THE GRAVES, ALL GAPING WIDE,
EVERY ONE LETS FORTH HIS SPRITE
IN THE CHURCH-WAY PATHS TO GLIDE.

AND WE FAIRIES THAT DO RUN
FROM THE PRESENCE OF THE SUN,
FOLLOWING DARKNESS LIKE A DREAM,
NOW ARE FROLIC.
I AM SENT WITH BROOM BEFORE...
TO SWEEP THE DUST BEHIND THE DOOR.

THROUGH THE HOUSE GIVE GLIMMERING LIGHT BY THE DEAD AND DROWSY FIRE.
EVERY ELF AND FAIRY SPRITE HOP AS LIGHT AS BIRD FROM BRIER.
AND THIS DITTY AFTER ME SING AND DANCE IT TRIPPINGLY.
HAND IN HAND, WITH FAIRY GRACE, WILL WE SING AND BLESS THIS PLACE.

NOW,
UNTIL THE BREAK OF DAY,

THROUGH THIS HOUSE EACH FAIRY STRAY.

TO THE BEST BRIDE-BED WILL WE, WHICH BY US SHALL BLESSED BE.

SO SHALL ALL THE COUPLES THREE EVER TRUE IN LOVING BE...

AND THE BLOTS OF
NATURE'S HAND
SHALL NOT
IN THEIR
ISSUE
STAND.
NEVER MOLE, HARE-LIP,
NOR SCAR, NOR MARK
PRODIGIOUS, SHALL
UPON THEIR
CHILDREN
BE.

WITH THIS FIELD-DEW CONSECRATE,
AND EACH SEVERAL CHAMBER BLESS...
THROUGH THIS PALACE WITH SWEET PEACE.
TRIP AWAY,
MAKE NO STAY,
MEET ME ALL BY BREAK OF DAY.

SHUF
SHUF
IF WE SHADOWS HAVE OFFENDED,
THINK BUT THIS, AND ALL IS MENDED,
THAT YOU HAVE BUT SLUMBERED HERE
WHILE THESE VISIONS DID APPEAR.
MND V.I.
AND THIS WEAK AND IDLE THEME, NO MORE YIELDING BUT A DREAM...
GENTLES, DO NOT REPREHEND.
IF YOU PARDON, WE WILL MEND.

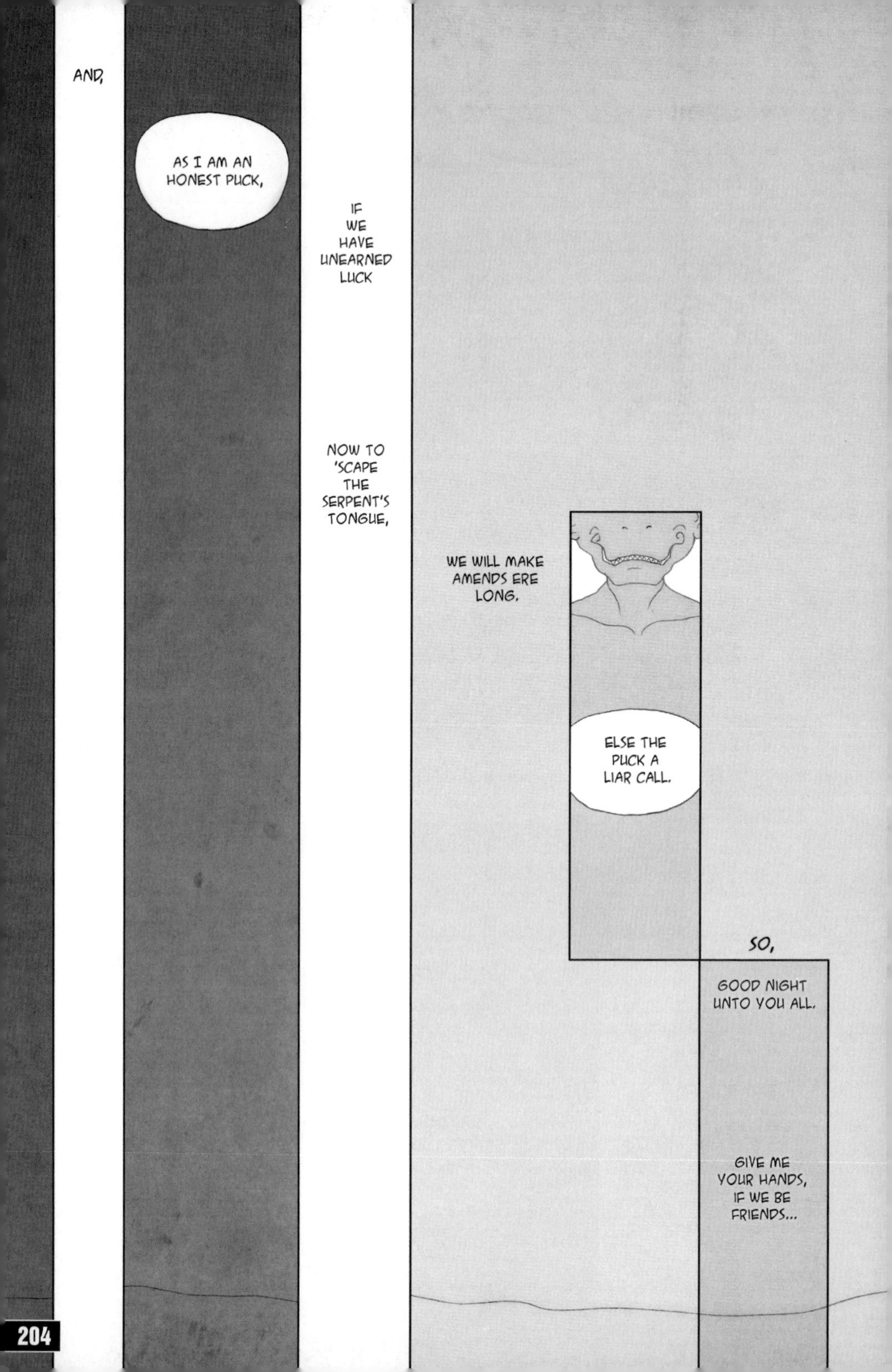

AND,

AS I AM AN HONEST PUCK,

IF WE HAVE UNEARNED LUCK

NOW TO 'SCAPE THE SERPENT'S TONGUE,

WE WILL MAKE AMENDS ERE LONG.

ELSE THE PUCK A LIAR CALL.

SO,

GOOD NIGHT UNTO YOU ALL.

GIVE ME YOUR HANDS, IF WE BE FRIENDS...

And Robin
shall restore
Amends

PLOT SUMMARY OF A MIDSUMMER NIGHT'S DREAM

Theseus, Duke of Athens, and Hippolyta, Queen of the Amazons, are arranging the celebrations for their forthcoming wedding on Midsummer Eve. Egeus spoils the festive mood by complaining to Theseus that his daughter Hermia has refused to marry Demetrius, the husband he has chosen for her, and invokes the Athenian law: she must either obey her father, or else be condemned to death – or to life as a nun. Hermia and her lover Lysander decide to elope, and confide their plans to Helena, Hermia's best friend, who is herself in love with Demetrius, despite his previously rejecting her for Hermia. Hoping to win Demetrius's favour, Helena now reveals their elopement to him. Total confusion follows as all four of them escape to the enchanted forest – Lysander and Hermia losing their way, Demetrius pursuing Hermia, and Helena pursuing Demetrius.

Oberon, King of the Fairies, and his Queen Titania are also in the forest, waiting to attend Theseus and Hippolyta's wedding. After a quarrel over Titania's refusal to surrender her Indian page-boy to him, Oberon seeks to punish her disobedience. He instructs the goblin Puck to drop the juice of a magical flower on the eyes of the sleeping Titania which will make her fall in love with the first creature she sees on waking. Puck is also ordered to do the same to Demetrius, whom Oberon has seen cruelly rejecting Helena – but the goblin mistakenly enchants Lysander instead, who wakes up and immediately falls in love with Helena. The confusion deepens as the lovers quarrel, and lose one another in the night-time maze of the forest.

Meanwhile, a group of Athenian workers have entered the forest to rehearse the inept play they are to perform at Theseus and Hippolyta's wedding, the inappropriately tragic story of *Pyramus and Thisbe*. Puck interrupts their rehearsal, however, and transforms the weaver Nick Bottom's head into a donkey's. Titania awakens to this sight, and lavishes her love on him, blissfully unaware though he remains of his transformation. Out of this comic chaos, order is gradually restored. Oberon gets his Indian page-boy, and releases Titania, Bottom, and the four Athenian lovers from their magical bondage. Demetrius at last proclaims his true love for Helena, leaving Hermia free to marry Lysander, since Theseus now overrules Egeus and commands the two reunited couples to join the ceremony of his own wedding to Hippolyta. The three happy couples enjoy the spectacle of the workers' ridiculously bad play before retiring for the night. The sleeping newlyweds are blessed with a happy future by the reconciled Oberon and Titania, the night's final visitors. But has it all been a dream?

A BRIEF LIFE OF WILLIAM SHAKESPEARE

Shakespeare's birthday is traditionally said to be the 23rd of April – St George's Day, patron saint of England. A good start for England's greatest writer. But that date and even his name are uncertain. He signed his own name in different ways. "Shakespeare" is now the accepted one out of dozens of different versions.

He was born at Stratford-upon-Avon in 1564, and baptized on 26th April. His mother, Mary Arden, was the daughter of a prosperous farmer. His father, John Shakespeare, a glove-maker, was a respected civic figure – and probably also a Catholic. In 1570, just as Will began school, his father was accused of illegal dealings. The family fell into debt and disrepute.

Will attended a local school for eight years. He did not go to university. The next ten years are a blank filled by suppositions. Was he briefly a Latin teacher, a soldier, a sea-faring explorer? Was he prosecuted and whipped for poaching deer?

We do know that in 1582 he married Anne Hathaway, eight years his senior, and three months pregnant. Two more children – twins – were born three years later but, by around 1590, Will had left Stratford to pursue a theatre career in London. Shakespeare's apprenticeship began as an actor and "pen for hire".

He learned his craft the hard way. He soon won fame as a playwright with often-staged popular hits.

He and his colleagues formed a stage company, the Lord Chamberlain's Men, which built the famous Globe Theatre. It opened in 1599 but was destroyed by fire in 1613 during a performance of *Henry VIII* which used gunpowder special effects. It was rebuilt in brick the following year.

Shakespeare was a financially successful writer who invested his money wisely in property. In 1597, he bought an enormous house in Stratford, and in 1608 became a shareholder in London's Blackfriars Theatre. He also redeemed the family's honour by acquiring a personal coat of arms.

Shakespeare wrote over 40 works, including poems, "lost" plays and collaborations, in a career spanning nearly 25 years. He retired to Stratford in 1613, where he died on 23rd April 1616, aged 52, apparently of a fever after a "merry meeting" of drinks with friends. Shakespeare did in fact die on St George's Day! He was buried "full 17 foot deep" in Holy Trinity Church, Stratford, and left an epitaph cursing anyone who dared disturb his bones.

There have been preposterous theories disputing Shakespeare's authorship. Some claim that Sir Francis Bacon (1561–1626), philosopher and Lord Chancellor, was the real author of Shakespeare's plays. Others propose Edward de Vere, Earl of Oxford (1550–1604), or, even more weirdly, Queen Elizabeth I. The implication is that the "real" Shakespeare had to be a university graduate or an aristocrat. Nothing less would do for the world's greatest writer.

Shakespeare is mysteriously hidden behind his work. His life will not tell us what inspired his genius.

EDITORIAL

Richard Appignanesi: Series Editor

Richard Appignanesi was a founder and co-director of the Writers & Readers Publishing Cooperative and Icon Books where he originated the internationally acclaimed *Introducing* series. His own best-selling titles written for the series include *Freud*, *Postmodernism* and *Existentialism*. He is also the author of the fiction trilogy *Italia Perversa* and the novel *Yukio Mishima's Report to the Emperor*. He is currently associate editor of the art and culture journal *Third Text* and reviews editor of the journal *Futures*. His latest book *What do Existentialists Believe?* was released in 2006.

Nick de Somogyi: Textual Consultant

Nick de Somogyi works as a freelance writer and researcher, as a genealogist at the College of Arms, and as a contributing editor to *New Theatre Quarterly*. He is the founding editor of the Globe Quartos series, and was the visiting curator at Shakespeare's Globe, 2003–6. His publications include *Shakespeare's Theatre of War* (1998), *Jokermen and Thieves: Bob Dylan and the Ballad Tradition* (1986), and, as editor, *The Little Book of War Poems* (1999), and (from 2001) the *Shakespeare Folios* series for Nick Hern Books. His other work has included contributions to the Open University (1995) and Carlton Television (2000), BBC Radio 3 and Radio 4, and the National Portrait Gallery (2006).

ARTIST

Kate Brown

Kate Brown is an independent illustrator, taking influence from comics around the world, including Japan's strong manga aesthetic. She graduated with a distinction from England's only Sequential Illustration course, specialising in Graphic Novels. Kate has been published multiple times, including stories in *Best New Manga,* and has completed work for *The Girly Comic*. As well as her illustration, Kate is also a writer with several major projects in development, currently collaborating with Paul Duffield (the artist for *The Tempest*). Kate closely follows the development of manga, and other comics, from around the world.

PUBLISHER

SelfMadeHero publishes manga and graphic novels. It launched its first titles in the Manga Shakespeare series with *Hamlet* and *Romeo and Juliet*. Other titles already published include: *Richard III* and *The Tempest*, with more to follow.

HAMLET

ROMEO AND JULIET

RICHARD III

THE TEMPEST

www.selfmadehero.com